Color Me, Cancer Free

Library of Congress Cataloging-in-Publication Data available upon request.

Luna Peak Publishing
Sierra Madre, CA | www.lunapeakpublishing.com
ISBN: 978-1-7355958-5-6

Printed and bound in the United States of America.
Cover art by Graciela Eastridge.

Color Me, Cancer Free:

a coloring book for

cool kids kicking cancer.

This activity book is inspired by the book

"Follow Me, Cancer Free"

by Melody Lomboy-Lowe and

illustrated by Graciela Eastridge

LUNA PEAK

I am so excited to share my story with you!

I am a childhood cancer survivor and the images are created by my friend and fellow cancer survivor, Graciela. We both had to go through many of the things you are going through right now. I hope you have fun reading, coloring and creating. This book will help you write your own version of "Follow Me, Cancer Free" that can give hope to a newly diagnosed cancer patient. Please share your creations with us and stay in touch with the Luna Peak Foundation community.

www.lunapeakfoundation.org

LUNA PEAK

Hello !

My Name is

MELODY!

COLOR ME,

CANCER FREE

Every Day I Make Sure to Help My Body Find a Cure

It is Important

to PLAY

It is Important

to REST

Important to

LISTEN

to those who

KNOW BEST

DOCTORS. and NURSES

with

EXPERT CARE

Help me Fight this Battle

that isn't Quite Fair

Every Day I Make

Sure I am

Ready to Fight

By Eating Healthy

and

Doing What's Right

I Also Need My
Friends and Family
to Help Me
Be CANCER FREE

Sometimes I Have to Get

an Awful

SHOT,

But When In Pain,

Think a

HAPPY THOUGHT

You and I Both Know

It's Not Easy

Especially on Days

I feel

EXTRA QUEASY

It's a Long Road Ahead

It Isn't All Bad.

You Will Be

Proud and Amazed

By The

STRENGTH

That You Had

So Keep Your

HEAD UP

and Be Sure to

Stay Strong

Even When You Feel

Like EVERYTHING

Is Going Wrong

You're a

SURVIVOR

Every Moment You Try,

Don't Waste Time

on Thinking

"WHY?"

MANY have

WON

The BATTLE

You Have Now

CHILDREN'S HOSP

You Will Look Back

At This Time

and

THINK to Yourself

"WOW!"

If We Can Do

THIS,

We Can Do

ANYTHING!

Just THINK, When You Are HEALTHY

You Will Feel

AMAZING!

My Cancer Journey is

Now Through,

It is Now Time

FOR YOU

To

SPREAD HOPE TOO!

THE END

Challenge yourself to complete each maze. Help Little Melody work through the maze to find the best outcome!

ur a
maze
ing!

CHILDREN'S HOSPIT

CELEBRATE LIFE WITH

LUNA PEAK!

WRITE YOUR OWN STORY!

Write about your days in the hospital, your friends, your family and your medical team. Write about what makes you happy, sad, frustrated and hopeful. You will love having these memories written down and hopefully you will share your story!

ALL ABOUT ME

Look its me!

My name is ____________________

I am __________ years old.

I am from ____________________

I am in Grade: ____________________

My birthday is: ____________________

My diagnosis: ____________________

My favorite things:

1. ____________________
2. ____________________
3. ____________________
4. ____________________
5. ____________________

things that make me happy

things that make me sad

MY STORY

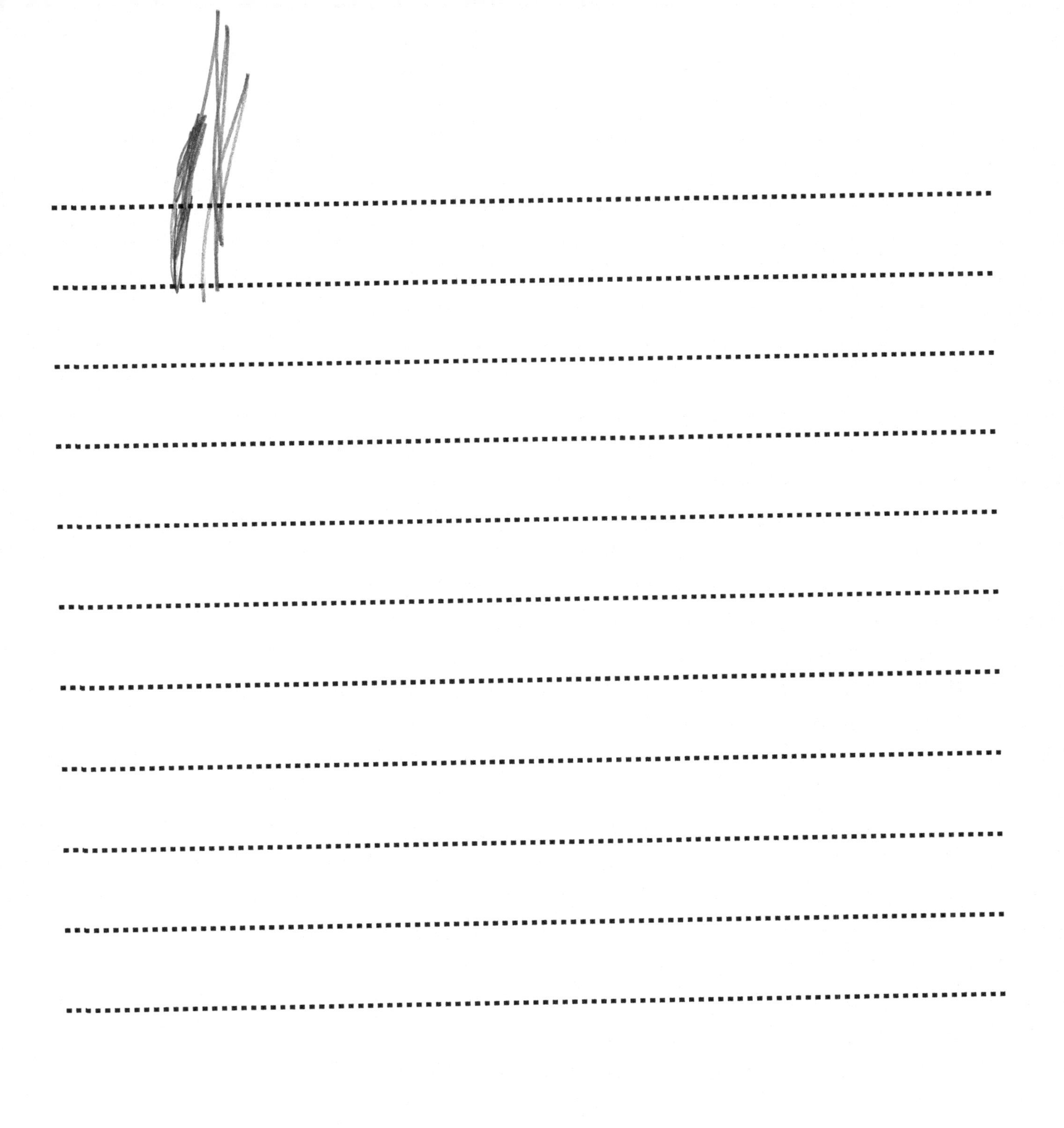

Made in the USA
Columbia, SC
06 January 2023